The Astrosmurf

Peyo

a SMURF adventure

The Astrosmurf

Written by DELPORTE and PEYO

Translated by Anthea Bell and Derek Hockridge

Random House 🏠 **New York**

YOU MAY HAVE MET THE SMURFS BEFORE. THEY ARE LITTLE BLUE PEOPLE, MUCH SMALLER THAN US HUMANS, AND THEY HAVE A LANGUAGE ALL THEIR OWN: THEY SPEAK SMURF LANGUAGE.

THERE'S PAPA SMURF, THE CHIEF SMURF OF ALL ...

BRAINY SMURF, WHO IS ALWAYS LECTURING PEOPLE ...

... AND REMEMBER, A SMURF IN TIME SAVES NINE, AND A ROLLING SMURF GATHERS NO SMURF ...

LAZY SMURF ...

GREEDY SMURF ...

CRUNCH CROC YUM YUM! SLURP GLUG GLUG BURP

GROUCHY SMURF, ETC., ETC. ....

I HATE ETCETERAS, ETC. ....

AND THEN THERE IS ONE STARRY-EYED LITTLE SMURF WHO GAZES AT THE STARRY SKY EVERY NIGHT.

Peyo 1

THIS SMURF HAS ONLY ONE WISH IN LIFE: HE WANTS TO BE A SPACE TRAVELER.

SIGH...

HE SEES HIMSELF VOYAGING THROUGH SPACE, REACHING A FANTASTIC WORLD WHERE SMURFY FOOT HAS NEVER TROD...

HIS DREAM BECOMES AN OBSESSION.

BUT HOW TO SMURF THERE? THAT IS THE SMURF.

?

HE CANNOT SLEEP...

SUPPOSE I BUILT A GREAT BIG CATAPULT TO... NO, IT WOULD NEVER SMURF!

...OR EAT...

I COULD SMURF SOME WINGS AND... NO. OH, SMURF, THIS ISN'T GOING TO BE EASY!

AND ONE DAY...

LABORATORY NO SMURFING AROUND

TAP TAP

OH, IT'S YOU. WHAT DO YOU WANT?

WELL, PAPA SMURF, I... I'D LIKE TO SMURF TO ANOTHER PLANET, BUT I CAN'T SEEM TO PLAN IT! ANY IDEAS?

HMM... WAIT A MINUTE! I SHOULD BE ABLE TO SMURF SOMETHING OF THE KIND IN MY BOOKS OF MAGIC!

YOU THINK SO? OH, DO LOOK!

ORATORY NO URFING ROUND

LET'S SEE... Astrology... Comets... Influence of the Moon... Shooting Stars...

QUICK! QUICK!

2

AH, HERE WE ARE! *How to Travel in the Macrocosm...* LISTEN TO THIS...

Firstly: every morning drink a pint of dew caught in the web of the male tarantula...

Secondly: Find a moonstone while the sun is in eclipse...

Thirdly: crush this stone carefully with your little finger, uttering cries of joy...

Fourthly: wait for the powdered moonstone to turn into salt. This may take a hundred years...

Fifthly: put a pinch of this salt on a comet's tail...

BANG!

Sixthly: at the same moment, get a tom cat to mew three times: MIAOWTOMEET—AMETEORITE. *Seventhly:* Do not be discouraged. *Eighthly...*

LABORATORY NO SMURFING AROUND

I'LL NEVER SMURF IT!

I'M...SNIFF! ...SO UNHAPPY! SNIFF!

HULLO...

BY SMURF, THIS GIVES ME AN IDEA! SUPPOSE I...YES!

I'M GOING TO SMURF A SHIP TO TAKE ME TO THE STARS!

Peyo 3

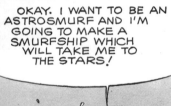

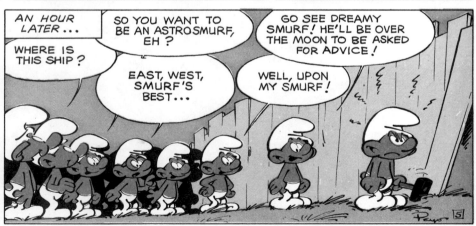

MANY DAYS PASS BY. ASTROSMURF IS HARD AT WORK BEHIND HIS FENCE...

NOW AND THEN HE CAN BE SEEN WALKING THROUGH THE VILLAGE CARRYING STRANGE OBJECTS...

YOUR SMURF-SHIP GETTING ON ALL RIGHT?

MMPH.

CAN WE SEE IT?

NO, NOT UNTIL IT'S QUITE SMURFED.

BUT THE SMURFS ARE CURIOUS...

WHOOSH

I SAID, NOT UNTIL IT'S QUITE SMURFED!

I'VE SEEN ASTROSMURF'S SMURFSHIP!

HOW DID YOU MANAGE THAT?

EASY! THERE'S A HOLE IN THE FENCE, AND I TOOK A SMURF THROUGH THAT.

I'M OFF TO SEE!

THAT'S RIGHT... A HOLE IN THE FENCE, GO AND LOOK!

6

...AND HE'S STAYED SMURFED UP IN HIS HOUSE FOR THREE DAYS NOW! HE WON'T SEE ANYONE EXCEPT PAPA SMURF!

POOR ASTROSMURF!

HERE COMES PAPA SMURF!

WELL?

HE'S JUST THE SAME...

KEEPS ON ABOUT HIS SHIP, AND THEN SUDDENLY HE WON'T SAY A SINGLE SMURF FOR HOURS ON END! I'M AFRAID HE MAY SUFFER A SMURFOUS BREAKDOWN IF THIS GOES ON.

BUT WHAT CAN WE SMURF ABOUT IT?

NOTHING! HE HITCHED HIS WAGON TO A SMURF, AND HE'LL NEVER BE HAPPY UNTIL HE CAN SMURF THE STARS HIMSELF! ALAS, THAT CAN NEVER SMURF...

UNLESS... WAIT! I MAY HAVE AN IDEA!

WHAT?

YOU MAY?

NOW, SMURF CAREFULLY TO ME! RIGHT! WE'RE GOING TO SMURF ASTROSMURF THAT HIS SHIP IS... AND.... ....

EVERYONE GET IT? OKAY, GO SMURF THE OTHERS!

THIS IS A SMURF IDEA!

11

NEXT DAY...

TAP TAP TAP

OH, HULLO, PAPA SMURF.

HULLO, ASTROSMURF!

I HAVE SOME GOOD SMURF FOR YOU!

YOU HAVE?

YES. HANDY SMURF HAS SMURFED OVER YOUR SHIP FROM TOP TO BOTTOM, TRYING TO FIND OUT WHY IT WOULDN'T SMURF THE OTHER DAY...

AND HE SMURFED WHAT WAS WRONG! HE'S PUT IT RIGHT, AND NOW IT SMURFS PERFECTLY! YOU CAN SMURF OFF FOR THE STARS WHENEVER YOU LIKE!

I CAN?

YIPPEE! JUST WAIT HERE! I'LL BE BACK IN A SMURF!

RIGHT, I'M READY! TRA-LA-LA! THIS IS THE SMURFIEST DAY OF MY LIFE!

COME ON, QUICK!

LET'S HOPE IT SMURFS OUT THE WAY WE PLANNED...

12

HERE! AND SMURF IT ALL UP THIS TIME. MIND YOU DON'T SPILL ANY!

GLUG GLUG GLUG

RIGHT! NOW, GET A SMURF ON! UP, YOU SMURF!

THAT'S IT! GOODBYE! GOODBYE!

AHA! HERE GOES!

RRRR

QUICK! THE PROPELLER'S STARTING TO SMURF! LIGHT THE FIRE! COME ON, YOU LOT, ROCK THAT SMURF-SHIP AS HARD AS YOU CAN!

FLAP FLAP FLAP

IT'S MOVING! I HAVE SMURF-OFF!

YIPPEE! THE CLOUDS! I'M ON SMURF NINE!

VRRRRRRRR

14

15

THERE, PAPA SMURF! WE'VE TAKEN IT TO PIECES!

GOOD!

SO NOW WHAT DO WE SMURF WITH ALL THE BITS?

WE'RE GOING TO SMURF THEM UP ON CARTS AND TAKE THEM TO A SPOT WHOSE WHEREABOUTS I ALONE SMURF!

IS IT FAR?

NO, ONLY ABOUT TWO DAYS JOURNEY!

!

THAT'S ENOUGH SMURF FOR TODAY. IT'S LATE! LET'S GO HOME!

I HAVE IMPORTANT SMURF TO DO TONIGHT, AND I DON'T WISH TO BE DISMURFED FOR ANY REASON AT ALL!

LABORATORY NO SMURFING AROUND

NOW LET'S SEE... WHERE'S THAT FORMULA? AH, HERE WE ARE!

...AND FOUR GRAINS OF HELLEBORE, SMURFED TO THE BOILING JUICE OF A MANDRAKE ROOT! THEN...

Euphorbia

NOW TO TRY IT OUT! I HOPE THAT WAS ALL SMURFWHILE!

SLURP

OH... OOOOH! FANTASTIC! TEEHEEHEE! IF THE SMURFS COULD SEE ME NOW...!

17

NEXT MORNING...

EVERYSMURF HERE? GOOD! FIRST, SMURF UP OUR STORES OF PROVISIONS AND CAMPING GEAR! WE'LL BE NEEDING THEM! THEN SMURF THE BITS OF THE SHIP INTO THE CARTS TOO!

OFF YOU GO. I'LL BE SMURFING YOU LATER. I MUST GO AND SEE ASTROSMURF.

STILL ASMURF?

SMURFING LIKE A LOG, PAPA SMURF!

RRRR

GOOD! GO SMURF A STRETCHER. WE'RE OFF!

ZZZZ

RRRR... RRRNF... HMM... SNURF...

WATCH OUT! HE'S WAKING UP! QUICK— MORE RASPBERRY JUICE!

GLUG GLUG GLUG GLUG GLUG

PHEW! I THOUGHT WE WERE SMURFED FOR THAT TIME!

RRRR... ZZZZ...

EVERYTHING READY? NOT FORSMURFED ANYTHING?

NO, PAPA SMURF.

GOOD! RIGHT, THEN... OFF WE GO!

18

PUSHING AND PULLING THEIR HEAVY CARTS, THE SMURFS PASS THROUGH FORESTS AND VALLEYS.

IS IT MUCH FARTHER, PAPA SMURF?

NO, NO! COME ON, BUCK UP! THINK HOW HAPPY ASTROSMURF WILL BE TO FIND HIS DREAM HAS COME SMURF! AND YOU'RE VERY FOND OF ASTROSMURF, AREN'T YOU?

THEY CROSS STREAMS...

IS IT MUCH FARTHER, PAPA SMURF?

NO, NO! NOT FAR NOW!

THEY CLIMB HILLS...

IS IT MUCH FARTHER, PAPA SMURF?

NOT FAR NOW...

WATCH OUT! ASTROSMURF IS WAKING UP!!

HELP!

THE RASPBERRY JUICE!

QUICK! QUICK!

TEEHEE HEE! HE WASN'T REALLY WAKING UP! SMURFED YOU THAT TIME, EH?

JOKEY SMURF!

NO SENSE OF HUMOR, THAT'S THEIR TROUBLE!

NIGHT FALLS, AND THE TIRED SMURFS CAMP OUT IN THE OPEN.

IS IT MUCH FARTHER, PAPA SMURF?

YES, IT IS!

WE'RE THERE!

ABOUT TIME TOO! NOW FOR A REST! WHAT A RELIEF!

RIGHT, GET TO WORK! WE MUST SMURF THE SHIP TOGETHER AGAIN!

!

AND WHILE WE'RE SMURFING ASTROSMURF'S SHIP TOGETHER AGAIN, JUST WHAT IS ASTROSMURF SMURFING, EH? *HE'S SLEEPING!*

ZZZ

GRUMBLEGRUMBLE... WHO SMURFS ABOUT HIM AND HIS STARS? @!✱✦! I SMURF YOU! OH, SMURF! I'VE SMURFED ABOUT ENOUGH OF THIS...

WHEW! IT'S FINISHED, PAPA SMURF!

RIGHT. PUT ASTROSMURF BACK AT THE CONTROLS!

AND DON'T FORGET TO SMURF HIM A LAST DRINK OF RASPBERRY JUICE!

CAREFUL DOES IT... THERE!

RRR ZZZ...

DONE IT? GOOD! HE'LL GO ON SMURFING FOR A WHILE NOW...

AND THAT WILL SMURF US TIME TO SETTLE IN. COME ON!

YOU MEAN WE'RE STAYING HERE?

BUT IF ASTROSMURF SMURFS US HERE, PAPA SMURF, HE'LL KNOW RIGHT AWAY HE ISN'T ON ANOTHER PLANET!

NO, HE WON'T, BECAUSE THANKS TO THE POTION I SMURFED THE OTHER NIGHT, WE'RE ALL GOING TO TURN INTO ...ER...WELL, LET'S CALL THEM *SWOOFS!*

?

?

I *HATE* SWOOFS!

22

LATER...

ZZZ

?

WHERE SMURF I ?

I CAN'T SEE A THING! IT'S ALL DARK!

WHAT'S SMURFED ? I REMEMBER I SUDDENLY FELT SMURFILY SLEEPY JUST AFTER I HAD SMURF-OFF, BUT WHAT THEN ?

OOOH!

I... I'M ON ANOTHER PLANET!!

23.

MY DREAM HAS COME SMURF! AT LAST! I'M SO HAPPY!

WHAT AN ASTROSMURFIC LANDSCAPE! THAT WAS ONE SMALL STEP FOR ME, A GIANT LEAP FOR SMURFKIND!

I WONDER IF THIS PLANET IS INHABITED?

KAYAAA! KAYAAA!

YES, IT IS!

NO, WAIT! I CAN'T SMURF OFF AGAIN WITHOUT EVEN FINDING OUT ABOUT THE SMURFS OF THIS PLANET!

AFTER ALL, THEY MAY BE FRIENDLY!

OH... LIGHTS!

WHAT DO I DO NOW? DO I SMURF THERE, OR DON'T I SMURF THERE?

I WILL SMURF THERE, SO THERE!

! !

WHOOSH

24

LISTEN, EVERYSWOOF! WE SHALL HOLD A GREAT SWOOF IN HONOR OF ASTROSMURF!

PHEW!

KAYAA!

WE'LL SWOOF MUSIC! A PARTY! DANCING!

I *HATE* PARTIES!

WHILE WE'RE WAITING FOR THE SWOOF TO BE READY, SWOOF US A BIT ABOUT THE PLANET WHERE YOU SWOOF FROM!

WELL, EARTH IS SMURFED MAINLY BY HUMAN BEINGS. THEY ARE VERY BIG AND NOT MUCH FUN. THEN THERE ARE US SMURFS. THERE ARE A HUNDRED OF US.

THERE'S GREEDY SMURF, AND JOKEY SMURF, AND LAZY SMURF, AND GROUCHY SMURF, AND BRAINY SMURF... HE'S ALWAYS SMURFING SERMONS AT US AND WAGGING HIS FINGER, LIKE THAT. HE'S A REAL SMURF IN THE NECK!

ME? BUT I...

PAF

AND THEN THERE'S PAPA SMURF. HE'S THE CHIEF SMURF OF ALL. HE HAS A BIG WHITE BEARD...

HE DOES?

WE ALL LIKE PAPA SMURF! HE'S VERY NICE! I DON'T KNOW WHAT WOULD BESMURF OF US BUT FOR PAPA SMURF...

THOUGH BETWEEN YOU AND ME, HE GETS ON OUR SMURFS A BIT SOMETIMES! BUT WE DON'T MIND. HE'S OLD, SO IT'S NOT SURPRISING HE SEEMS A BIT GAGA NOW AND SMURF...

WHAT DID I SAY? WHAT'S THE MATTER WITH THEM?

EVERYTHING'S READY, GRANDPA SWOOF! WE CAN SWOOF THE BIG PARTY!

27

HULLO... DAY IS BREAKING! TIME TO GO SWOOF!

YOU CAN SWOOF HERE!

THREE CHEERS FOR ASTROSMURF... SWOOF SWOOF...

HURRAY!

THERE!

!

AND SWOOF WELL, BECAUSE YOU'LL NEED PLENTY OF STRENGTH TO SWOOF BACK TO YOUR OWN PLANET TOMORROW.

OH, BUT I'M NEVER GOING TO SMURF BACK TO EARTH! I'M FAR TOO HAPPY HERE WITH YOU. I'VE DECIDED TO SMURF HERE FOR GOOD!

WHAT? BUT... BUT YOU CAN'T! I ... WE...

RRRRR ZZZ!

OH NO! THAT PUTS THE LID ON IT!

WELL, IS HE PLEASED, PAPA SMURF?

I'LL SAY! SO PLEASED HE WANTS TO SMURF HERE FOR GOOD!

DOES THAT MEAN WE'LL HAVE TO MAKE OUT WE'RE SWOOFS ALL OUR LIVES?

WE CAN'T! WE'LL HAVE TO SMURF HIM THE TRUTH!

WAIT! I HAVE AN IDEA!

29

LATER...

AAAH! I SMURFED LIKE A LOG! WHAT A LOVELY PLANET!

HULLO THERE! SMURF AND ABOUT ALREADY?

WATCH OUT! HERE HE COMES!

WELL, ASTROSMURF, DO YOU STILL WANT TO SWOOF HERE FOR GOOD?

OH YES, GRANDPA SWOOF!

ALL RIGHT, BUT MIND, IF YOU WANT TO BESWOOF ONE OF THE SWOOFS, YOU MUST PROVE YOUR COURAGE AND SKILL!

I MUST? WELL, WHAT DO I HAVE TO SMURF, THEN?

OH, IT'S SIMPLE ENOUGH! EYES BLINDFOLDED, YOU TURN ROUND THREE TIMES AND SWOOF THIS SPEAR RIGHT INTO THE BULL'S-EYE!

SURE YOU CAN'T SWOOF ANYTHING?

NOT A THING!

ONE... TWO... THREE...

GO ON!

HERE SMURFS!

DZONG

TCHAC

I DID IT! I DID IT!

SO NOW I'M A SWOOF, GRANDPA SWOOF! RIGHT?

ER... WELL...

NO, NOT YET! YOU'VE ONLY SWOOFED THE FIRST TEST!

SWOOF FOR US HERE A MOMENT. WE HAVE THINGS TO SWOOF!

OH, SMURF! WHAT ROTTEN LUCK!

WE MUST SMURF OF SOMETHING ELSE!

YES, BUT WHAT?

SUPPOSE WE MADE HIM SMURF A GREASY POLE?

SMURF IDEA! SOMEONE GO GREASE A POLE!

COME ON!

RIGHT! FOR YOUR SECOND TEST, YOU MUST SWOOF A POLE!

OH, THAT'S EASY! I ALWAYS WIN POLE-SMURFING COMPETITIONS AT HOME.

IT'S READY, GRANDPA SWOOF!

31

A TALL ONE, EH?

I'VE SMURFED TALLER IN MY TIME!

WELL, OFF YOU GO, THEN, AND GOOD SWOOF!

DONE IT! HERE I AM!

OH, SMURF! THAT POLE WASN'T SMURFED AT ALL!

WHAT? YOU MEAN YOU NEVER SMURFED IT...

I THOUGHT HE WAS GOING TO...

WHAT, ME? NO, YOU WERE GOING TO SMURF IT, WEREN'T YOU?

ME?

HEY, CAN I COME DOWN?

WHAT? NO, NOT YET.

WHAT NOW? WE'RE REALLY UP THE SMURF!

I'VE GOT AN IDEA FOR ANOTHER TEST ... I'M SURE THIS ONE WILL SMURF!

WHAT IS IT?

ALL RIGHT, YOU CAN SWOOF DOWN NOW.

LISTEN, GRANDPA SWOOF, YOU KNOW WHAT WE SMURF AT HOME WHEN WE WANT TO PLAY A TRICK ON A SMURF? WE SMURF THE POLE WITH GREASE! HA, HA, HA! FUNNY, ISN'T IT?

32

YOU MUST NOW SWOOF YOUR STRENGTH BY FIGHTING A SWOOF!

OH.

I'LL SWOOF YOUR OPPONENT AT RANDOM... LET'S SEE...

OH, BOTHER! THEY ALL LOOK THE SAME, SMURFED UP LIKE SWOOFS!

NO, THAT'S JOKEY SMURF!

AND THAT'S LAZY SMURF!

GREEDY SMURF!

BRAINY SMURF... LOOKS A LOT DIMMER WITHOUT GLASSES!

GROUCHY SMURF...

ROCKER SMURF...

GOOD, THAT'S HIM! HEFTY SMURF!

WELL, LET'S SAY THIS SWOOF, SHALL WE?

RIGHT!

WHAT, ME?

YOU MADE A MISSMURF, PAPA SMURF! YOU PICKED VANITY SMURF!

!

WELL, READY?

BING PIF OUCH! PAF OUCH! SLAM

QUICK! ANOTHER TEST! ANY IDEAS? QUICK!

33

WELL DONE! I HOPE YOU SWOOF THE NEXT TEST JUST AS WELL!

YOU MEAN THERE ARE *STILL* SOME MORE TESTS?

SURE, UNTIL YOU... ER... WELL, SEE THOSE MOUNTAINS? THERE'S EDELWEISS SWOOFING ON TOP OF THEM. YOU MUST BRING BACK AN EDELWEISS FLOWER BEFORE NIGHTFALL!

BUT... THERE ISN'T MUCH OF TODAY LEFT AND...

EXACTLY! GET A MOVE ON! YOU'RE SWOOFING TIME!

PUFF... PUFF... I'LL NEVER SMURF IT...

OH, A STORK! NOW IF THEY'RE AS SMURFFUL HERE AS THEY ARE ON EARTH, I MAY HAVE A CHANCE!

HEY!

AHA! THE SUN WILL SOON SMURF BELOW THE HORIZON!

AND ASTROSMURF ISN'T BACK YET!

IT SMURFED ALL RIGHT THIS TIME!

YOOHOO! HERE I COME!

AND HERE'S AN EDELWEISS FLOWER!

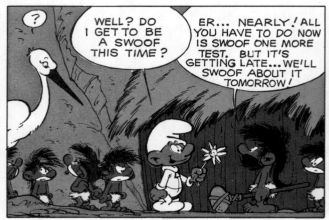

?

WELL? DO I GET TO BE A SWOOF THIS TIME?

ER... NEARLY! ALL YOU HAVE TO DO NOW IS SWOOF ONE MORE TEST. BUT IT'S GETTING LATE... WE'LL SWOOF ABOUT IT TOMORROW!

AND THAT NIGHT, WHILE ASTROSMURF IS ASLEEP...

RRR... ZZZ...

OH YES! WHAT A GOOD IDEA! IT CAN'T GO SMURF THIS TIME!

NEXT DAY...

HULLO! SMURF WELL? HOW ABOUT THIS LAST TEST OF YOURS?

WELL, ALL YOU HAVE TO DO IS SHOW YOU'RE CAPABLE OF SWOOFING THE HARSH AND RIGOROUS LIFE OF THE SWOOFS. YOU'LL HAVE TO SWOOF THE MEALS...

... FOR THE WHOLE TRIBE, SWOOF THE DISHES AFTERWARDS, AND SWEEP AND CLEAN AND SCRUB, AND YOU MUSTN'T SWOOF A WORD THE WHOLE TIME!

OH DEAR!

AND THAT'S NOT ALL! YOU MUST PROSTRATE YOURSELF BEFORE EVERY SWOOF YOU MEET, AND YOU HAVE TO SWOOF HIS FEET!

I DO?

YOU HAVE TO SWOOF ON A BED OF SHARP STONES, AND GET UP THREE TIMES A NIGHT TO SWOOF ROUND THE CAMP, WITHOUT SINGING OR WHISTLING... HOWEVER HAPPY YOU FEEL!

BUT...

ALL YOU'RE ALLOWED TO SWOOF FOR YOUR OWN MEALS IS EDELWEISS...

ALL YOU CAN DRINK IS OIL...

AND ONLY ONCE A DAY.

IN YOUR SPARE TIME YOU'LL BE SWOOFING IN THE SALT MINES!

AND YOU HAVE TO KEEP THIS UP FOR SWOOFTY-FIVE HUNDRED AND FORTY-THREE DAYS!

AND YOU MUSTN'T COMPLAIN.

WITH THE TASTE OF SWOOF ON YOUR LIPS!

OF COURSE YOU WON'T BE ALLOWED TO JOIN THE SWOOFING ON HOLIDAYS!

SO ONLY YOU CAN SWOOF IF YOU'RE REALLY FIT TO BE A SWOOF!

ER... WELL... WHEN ALL'S SMURFED AND DONE, I EXPECT PAPA SMURF MAY BE A BIT WORRIED I HAVEN'T SMURFED BACK. I ... I THINK I'D REALLY BETTER BE SMURFING BACK TO EARTH!

OOF!

36

Peyo

RIGHT, COME ON! THE FIRST THING TO SWOOF ... I MEAN SMURF... IS TO TAKE THE ANTIDOTE WHICH WILL TURN US BACK INTO SMURFS!

A LITTLE LATER...

I FEEL MUCH SMURFER LIKE THIS!

NOW WHAT? SMURF THE SHIP TO PIECES AND TAKE IT HOME, OF COURSE!

AT THIS RATE, WE'LL BE GOING TO PIECES!

AFTER THE LONG JOB OF DISMANTLING ...

...A LONG JOURNEY HOME...

IS IT MUCH FARTHER, PAPA SMURF?

...AND A LONG JOB OF REASSEMBLY...

DONE IT, PAPA SMURF! AND WE'VE SMURFED ASTRO-SMURF BACK UP IN THE CAPSULE!

GOOD!

NOW WE JUST HAVE TO SMURF PATIENTLY TILL HE WAKES UP.

WELL, IS HE EVER SMURFING OUT OR NOT? THIS WAS ABOUT ALL WE SMURFED!

HERE HE COMES!

LONG LIVE ASTROSMURF! THREE SMURFS FOR ASTROSMURF!

Peyo

38

PAPA SMURF! YOU'VE NO IDEA HOW SMURF I AM TO SEE YOU!

SAME HERE! WELL, HOW WAS IT?

GREAT! AMAZING! ABSOSMURFLY FANTASTIC! I'VE BEEN TO A PLANET INHABITED BY SWOOFS!

NEVER!

THE SWOOFS ARE RATHER PRIMITIVE, BUT VERY NICE. WHENEVER I SMURFED THROUGH THEIR CAMP THEY PROSTRATED THEMSELVES BEFORE ME!

AND THEY SMURFED A BIG PARTY FOR ME. I SAT ON GRANDPA SWOOF'S RIGHT HAND. GRANDPA SWOOF WAS OKAY, EVEN IF HE DID PUT ON AIRS TO MAKE HIMSELF SEEM SMURF...

TEEHEEHEE!

AND NEXT DAY I SHOWED THEM WHAT SMURFS CAN DO! I SMURFED A SPEAR RIGHT INTO THE BULL'S-EYE. I WON A FIGHT WITH A VERY BIG STRONG SWOOF, HE MUST HAVE SWOOFED AT LEAST TWO FEET TALL...

BUT I'M SMURFLY MORE THAN...

SSH!

THE SWOOFS WANTED ME TO STAY, BUT I WAS FEELING SMURFSICK, SO I CAME BACK.

YOU'RE NOT THINKING OF SMURFING AWAY AGAIN, ARE YOU?

WELL, TO TELL YOU THE TRUTH, THE THOUGHT OF SMURFING OTHER PLANETS IS TEMPTING, BUT...

... BUT I FEEL I SHOULD NEVER BE SO SMURF ANYWHERE AS HERE. SO I'M GOING TO SMURF MY SHIP TO PIECES!

VERY SENSIBLE TOO! AND WE'LL SMURF A BIG PARTY TO CELEBRATE YOUR RETURN TO SMURF!

YIPPEE!

DAYS PASS BY... LIFE IS BACK TO NORMAL, CALM AND PEACEFUL.

YOU KNOW, I THINK ASTRO-SMURF'S IDEA WAS SMURFWHILE AFTER ALL!

YEAH... MUST BE GREAT, SMURFING ABOUT IN SPACE, BEING A "STAR"!

IT WAS A PITY HIS SMURFSHIP DIDN'T SMURF TOO WELL!

NOW IN HIS PLACE, I WOULDN'T HAVE SMURFED A PROPELLER AS A MEANS OF PROPULSMURF!

FOR INSTANCE, I MIGHT HAVE MIXED SULFUR, SALTPETER AND CHARCOAL IN A PIPE, AND WHEN IT WENT SMURF THAT WOULD HAVE SENT THE SHIP SMURFING INTO SPACE!

YOU KNOW, THAT'S NOT A BAD IDEA! I'VE A GOOD SMURF TO TRY...

NO! NO! WE'RE NOT SMURFING THAT OVER AGAIN!

THE END

40